Typesetting by Creative Design & Typesetting
Reproduction & printing in the UK

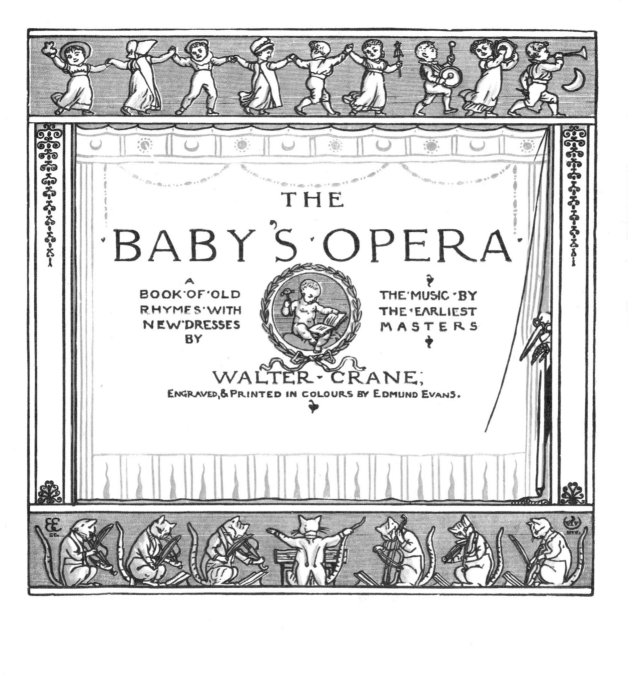

THE BABY'S OPERA

A BOOK OF OLD RHYMES WITH NEW DRESSES BY

THE MUSIC BY THE EARLIEST MASTERS

WALTER · CRANE;

ENGRAVED, & PRINTED IN COLOURS BY EDMUND EVANS.

CONTENTS

Girls and boys come out to play,
The moon doth shine as bright as day;
Come with a whoop, and come with a call,
Come with a good will or not at all.

Leave your sup-per, and leave your sleep;
Come to your playfellows in the street;
Up the lad-der and down the wall,
A pen-ny loaf will serve you all.

THE MULBERRY BUSH

Here we go round the mul-berry bush, the mul-berry bush, the mulberry bush;

Here we go round the mulberry bush, All on a fros-ty morn - ing.

This is the way we clap our hands, This is the way we clap our hands,

This is the way we clap our hands, All on a fros-ty morn - ing.

· HERE · WE · GO · ROVND · THE · MVLBERRY · BVSH ·

ORANGES & LEMONS

Oran-ges and le-mons, says the bells of St. Clemen's; You owe me five farthings, says the
D.C. When will that be? says the bells of Step-ney; I do not know, says the

bells of St. Mar-tin's; When will you pay me, says the bells of Old Bai-ley;
great bell of Bow.

When I grow rich, says the bells of Shore-ditch; Here comes a can-dle to

D.C.

light you to bed, And here comes a chop-per to chop off your head.

ST. PAUL'S STEEPLE

Up - on Paul's stee - ple stands a tree As full of ap - ples as may be, The lit - tle boys of Lon - don town They run with hooks to pull them down; And then they run from hedge to hedge Un - til they come to Lon - don Bridge.

5

MY LADY'S GARDEN

How does my la - - dy's gar - den grow? How does my la - - dy's gar - den grow? With sil - - ver bells, and coc - kle shells, And pret - ty maids all in a row!.......

7

·NATURAL·HISTORY·

1. What are lit - tle boys made of?
2. What are lit - tle girls made of?

What are lit - tle boys made of? Frogs and snails and
What are lit - tle girls made of? Su - gar and spice and

pup - py-dog's tails, And that are lit - tle boys made of.
all that's nice, And that are lit - tle girls made of.

3. What are young men made of?
What are young men made of?
Sighs and leers, and crocodile tears,
And that are young men made of.

4. What are young women made of?
What are young women made of?
Ribbons and laces, and sweet pretty faces,
And that are young women made of.

·LAVENDER'S · BLUE·

La - ven -der's blue, did-dle, did-dle! La - ven - der's green;

When I am king, did-dle, diddle! You shall be queen.

2. Call up your men, diddle, diddle!
   Set them to work;
   Some to the plough, diddle, diddle!
   Some to the cart.

3. Some to make hay, diddle, diddle!
   Some to cut corn;
   While you and I, diddle, diddle!
   Keep ourselves warm.

I SAW THREE SHIPS

1. I saw three ships come sail - ing by,
2. And what do you think was in them then,

Sail - ing by, sail - ing by, I saw three ships come
In them then, in them then, And what do you think was

sail - ing by, On New-year's Day in the morn - - ing.
in them then, On New-year's Day in the morn - - ing?

3. Three pretty girls were in them then,
   In them then, in them then,
   Three pretty girls were in them then,
   On New-year's Day in the morning.

4. And one could whistle, and one could sing,
   The other play on the violin;
   Such joy there was at my wedding,
   On New-year's Day in the morning.

I·SAW· THREE·SHIPS·

11

DING·DONG·BELL

Ding dong bell! Pus-sy's in the well! Who put her in? Lit-tle Tommy Lin.

Who pulled her out? Lit-tle Tommy Stout. What a naughty boy was that To

drown poor pussy-cat, Who ne'er did any harm, But killed all the mice in fa-ther's barn.

THREE·BLIND·MICE·

Three blind mice,... See how they run! They
all ran af-ter the farmer's wife, Who cut off their tails with a car-ving knife; Did
e-ver you hear such a thing in your life?.... Three blind mice...

· DICKORY · DOCK ·

Hick - o - ry, dick - o - ry dock!......... The mouse ran

up the clock;......... The clock struck one, The

mouse ran down, Hick - o - ry, dick - o - ry dock!.........

15

Y^e FROG'S WOOING

1. It was the frog lived in the well, Heigh - ho! says Row - ley; And the mer - ry mouse un - der the mill, With a Row - ley, Pow - ley, Gammon, and Spinach, Heigh - ho! says Anthony Row - ley.

2.
The frog he would a-wooing ride, Heigh-ho, &c.
Sword and buckler at his side, With a, &c.

3.
When upon his high horse set, Heigh-ho, &c.
His boots they shone as black as jet, With a, &c.

4.
When he came to the merry mill-pin, Heigh-ho, &c.
"Lady Mouse, are you within?" With a, &c.

5.
Then came out the dusty mouse, Heigh-ho, &c
"I am the lady of this house," With a, &c.

6.
"Hast thou any mind of me?" Heigh-ho, &c.
"I have e'en great mind of thee," With a, &c.

7.
"Who shall this marriage make?" Heigh-ho, &c.
"Our lord, which is the rat," With a, &c.

8.
"What shall we have to our supper?" Heigh-ho, &c.
"Three beans in a pound of butter," With a, &c.

9.
But when the supper they were at, Heigh-ho, &c.
The frog, the mouse, and e'en the rat, With a, &c.

10.
Then came in Tib, our cat, Heigh-ho, &c.
And caught the mouse e'en by the back, With a, &c

11.
Then did they separate, Heigh-ho, &c.
The frog leaped on the floor so flat, With a, &c.

12.
Then came in Dick, our drake, Heigh-ho, &c.
And drew the frog e'en to the lake, With a, &c.

13.
The rat he ran up the wall, Heigh-ho, &c.
And so the company parted all, With a, &c

1. Dame, get up and bake your pies,
   Bake your pies, bake your pies;
   Dame, get up and bake your pies,
   On Christmas-day in the morning.

2. Dame, what makes your maidens lie,
   Maidens lie, maidens lie?
   Dame, what makes your maidens lie,
   On Christmas-day in the morning?

3. Dame, what makes your ducks to die,
   Ducks to die, ducks to die?
   Dame, what makes your ducks to die,
   On Christmas-day in the morning?

4. Their wings are cut, they cannot fly,
   Cannot fly, cannot fly;
   Their wings are cut, they cannot fly,
   On Christmas-day in the morning.

18

·LITTLE ·JACK·HORNER·

Lit - tle Jack Hor - ner sat in a cor - ner, Eat - ing a
Christ - mas pie; .... He put in his thumb, and
pulled out a plum, And said, "What a good boy am I!" ....

KING ARTHVR

1. When good King Ar-thur ruled this land, He
was a good-ly king— He stole three pecks of
bar-ley-meal, To make a bag pud-ding.

2. A bag pudding the Queen did make,
   And stuffed it well with plums,
   And in it put great lumps of fat
   As big as my two thumbs.

3. The King and Queen did eat thereof,
   And noblemen beside,
   And what they could not eat that night
   The Queen next morning fried.

A R

Yᵉ JOLLY MILLER

There was a jol-ly mil-ler once Lived on the ri-ver Dee;.... He worked and sang from morn till night, No lark more blithe than he...... And this the bur-den of his song For e-ver used to be,...... "I care for no-bo-dy, no, not I, And no-bo-dy cares for me.".....

Y^e SONG oF SIXPENCE

1. Sing a song of six - pence, a   pocket full of rye;   Four and twenty

black - birds   baked in a   pie;   When the pie was o - pen the

birds be-gan to   sing,   Was-n't that a dain-ty dish to   set be-fore the king?

2. The king was in his counting-house counting out his money;
The queen was in the parlour eating bread and honey;
The maid was in the garden hanging out her clothes,
When up came a blackbird and pecked off her nose.

1. Lit-tle Bo-Peep, she lost her sheep, And did-n't know where to find them; Let them a-lone, they'll all come home And bring their tails be-hind them.

2. Little Bo-Peep fell fast asleep,
   And dreamt she heard them bleating;
   But when she awoke, she found it a joke,
   For they were still a-fleeting.

3. Then up she took her little crook,
   Determined for to find them,
   She found them indeed, but it made her
      heart bleed
   For they'd left their tails behind them.

4. It happened one day as Bo-Peep did stray
   Into a meadow hard by,
   There she espied their tails side by side,
   All hung on a tree to dry.

5. She heaved a sigh and wiped her eye,
   Then went o'er hill and dale,
   And tried what she could, as a shep-
      herdess should,
   To tack to each sheep its tail.

LITTLE
BO·PEEP

25

TOM, THE PIPER'S SON

Tom, Tom, the pi-per's son, Stole a pig and a - way did run; The pig was eat, and Tom was beat, And Tom went roar-ing down the street.

·OVER·THE·HILLS·&·FAR·AWAY·

1. Tom he was a piper's son, He learnt to play when he was young; But all the tunes that he could play Was "O - ver the hills and far a - way."

O - ver the hills and a great way off, The wind shall blow my top-knot off.

2. Tom with his pipe made such a noise
That he pleased both the girls and boys,
And they stopped to hear him play,
" Over the hills and far away."
Over the hills, &c.

COCK ROBIN AND JENNY WREN

1. 'Twas on a mer-ry time, When Jenny Wren was young, So neat-ly as she
2. " My dearest Jen-ny Wren, If you will but be mine, You shall dine on cher-ry

danced, And so sweet-ly as she sung, Rob-in Redbreast lost his heart, He
pie, And drink nice currant wine ; I'll dress you like a gold-finch Or

was a gallant bird, He doffed his cap to Jenny Wren, Requesting to be heard.
like a peacock gay, So if you'll have me, Jenny, dear, Let us appoint the day."

3. Jenny blushed behind her fan
   And thus declared her mind—
   " So let it be to-morrow, Rob,
   " I'll take your offer kind ;
   " Cherry pie is very good,
   " And so is currant wine,
   " But I will wear my plain brown gown,
   " And never dress too fine."

4. Robin Redbreast got up early,
   All at the break of day,
   He flew to Jenny Wren's house,
   And sang a roundelay ;
   He sang of Robin Redbreast,
   And pretty Jenny Wren,
   And when he came unto the end,
   He then began again.

29

I
HAD·A·LITTLE·
NVT·TREE

I had a lit - tle nut - tree, no - thing would it bear

But a sil-ver nut -meg and a gold-en pear; The King of Spain's daughter

came to vi - sit me, And all for the sake of my lit - tle nut - tree.

·I·HAD·A· LITTLE

·NVT· TREE·

31

MY·PRETTY·MAID·

1. "Where are you going to, my pret-ty maid? Where are you going to, my pretty maid?" "I'm go-ing a-milk-ing, Sir," she said, "Sir," she said, "Sir," she said, "I'm go-ing a-milk-ing, Sir," she said.

2. "Shall I go with you, my pretty maid?"
"Yes, if you please, kind Sir," she said,
"Sir," she said, "Sir," she said,
"Yes, if you please, kind Sir," she said.

3. "What is your fortune, my pretty maid?"
"My face is my fortune, Sir," she said,
"Sir," she said, "Sir," she said,
"My face is my fortune, "Sir," she said.

4. "Then I can't marry you, my pretty maid."
"Nobody asked you, Sir," she said,
"Sir,' she said, "Sir," she said,
"Nobody asked you, Sir," she said.

'WHERE ARE YOU
GOING TO MY
PRETTY MAID?'

Jack and Jill went up the hill To fetch a
pail of wa - ter; Jack fell down and
broke his crown, And Jill came tum - bling af - ter.

JACK & JILL.

DANCE A BABY

Dance a ba-by did-dy!..... What can
mam-my do wid-'e?...... Sit in her lap,
Give it some pap, And dance a ba-by did-dy!....

HUSH-A-BY BABY

Hush - a - by ba - by on the tree - top, When the wind
blows the cra - dle will rock; When the bough breaks the
cra - dle will fall— Down comes ba - by, cra - dle and all!

·KING· ·COLE·

Old King Cole was a mer-ry old soul, And a mer-ry old soul was he; He

called for his pipe, and he called for his bowl, And he called for his fid - dlers three.

Ev - 'ry fid - dler had a fid-dle, And a ve-ry fine fid-dle had he.

Tweedle dee, tweedle dee, tweedle dee, tweedle dee,
Tweedle dee, tweedle dee, went the fid - dlers three,
O there's none so rare as can com- pare

With King Cole and his fid - dlers three.

FINIS

·KING·COLE·